To Mo and Paul,
who know how to be them.

Text and illustrations copyright © Mary Murphy 2020

Designed by Andrew Watson

First published in Great Britain in 2020 by
Otter-Barry Books, Little Orchard, Burley Gate, Herefordshire, HR1 3QS
www.otterbarrybooks.com

ISBN 978 1 910959 25 1

Illustrations created with brush and ink, and digitally

Handlettered type by Mary Murphy

Printed in China

9 8 7 6 5 4 3 2 1

Only a Tree
knows how
to be a tree

Mary Murphy

A tree has leaves
that turn sunshine
into tree food.
Amazing!

Later,
the leaves
change colour

and

twirl

to

the

ground.

A tree gives shelter.
It can be a home.

Only a tree knows
how to be a tree.

Birds build
nests for homes.

They sing
different songs

and their babies
hatch from eggs.

Best of all,
they can fly.

Only a bird knows
how to be a bird.

Dogs are our friends.
They play with us and love us.

They wag their tails and move
their ears to show us how they feel.
They flip water into their mouths to drink.

I can't do that, but then
only a dog knows
how to be a dog.

Water has no colour,
but you can see it.
It makes rivers and sea,
clouds and rain and snow.

Fish live in water.
They flash like jewels.

Everyone needs water,
and only water knows
how to be water.

Only fish know how to be fish.

Earth is where we live,
with all the plants,
animals, oceans,
mountains and rivers.

It turns around
to give us day and night.
It tilts through the year,
to give us seasons.

There are countless stars
in the universe
and many, many planets.

But Earth is our home,
and only Earth knows how to be Earth.

Every comet,

flower,

cat

and beetle,

every cloud,

frog,

stone
and duck,

every mountain,

river

and deer is different,

and every tree is different.

And they are all the only ones
who know how to be them.

As for people, there are billions of us.

We learn to eat and talk,
to sing and walk.

We work. We play. We tell stories.

Every person
has their own thoughts
in their head
and their own feelings
in their heart.

Every single person is different.
And only they know how to be them.

Only I know how to be me.

And only you know how to be you.